Genesis In Rhyme

18 Favorite Stories as told by Mikel Waldon

CPW LLC

Published by CPW LLC 2009.

Printed in Hong Kong.

Library of Congress Control Number 2009900622

Waldon, Mikel
Genesis In Rhyme/ by Mikel Waldon: illustrated by Michael Graham

Edited by Norma Hopcraft and Katina Austin

ISBN 978-0-9818387-0-0

GENESIS
IN RHYME

18 Favorite Stories
As Told by Mikel Waldon
Illustrated by Michael Graham

Dedication

This book is dedicated to those who have supported and encouraged my efforts, not the least of whom is my lovely wife Karen. Without her encouragement, this would have continued to reside in my "one day I'll do it" folder. I also appreciate the input and proofing by my daughter Katina and my son Isaac. And of course, I must dedicate this book to my sweet little daughter Sarah and my new grandson Cormac, who I trust have many years of great reading ahead!

Table of Contents

Creation Story

Genesis 1:1- :3

In the long ago past, 'twas so black you could feel it.
There was nothing but God and His Son and His Spirit.
Well, then God had a thought that some light might be fun,
so He brightened things up, and He called it day one.

Guess what? Next, God decided some sky He would love,
so He spoke and created it, there—up above.
And though only day two of what soon would be seven,
He'd divided the waters and called the space Heaven.

Now God next set about raising land if you please,
as He gathered the waters and called them the seas.
Then it hit Him that green was a color still free,
so He made shrubs and trees and then finished day three.

Well, so far everything that He'd done was just fine,
but He thought it'd be nice if He added some shine,
so one sun and one moon and the stars all galore,
He hung them in space and He called that day four.

Now just on a hunch, or perhaps on a whim,
God filled up the seas with the things that can swim.
And to cap off day five God placed things in the sky,
lots of colored winged birds that He taught how to fly.

Next He made many creatures to fill in the land;
then He had one more thought that would finish His plan.
So He took up some dust, I believe in His hand,
and He fashioned it into the shape of a man.

Now that's it; in six days God made all that there is,
and the glory and honor was certainly His.
Then He smiled as He looked over all earth and heaven;
He had finished—He rested—and called that day seven.

2

Adam and Eve

Genesis 3:1-24

As you know and have heard, God made Adam from dust,
but it soon became clear a help-mate was a must.
So He took Adam's rib without using a knife,
and from it shaped Eve and gave Adam his wife.

Now one day as Eve wandered 'round through the garden
a slimy old snake slithered up and said, "Pardon,
did God tell you not to eat fruit from the trees?"
And Eve answered back, "Not at all, if you please."

"God told us there's only one tree to avoid."
At this the snake seemed to get rather annoyed.
He said, "God's just scared that you'll get smart like He."
So Eve ate some fruit from that forbidden tree.

Now Adam came up to around where Eve stood,
and saw that the fruit that she had looked real good,
so he ate of the fruit she herself had just had
and at once they discovered the good and the bad.

For the first time they realized that naked they were.
They fashioned some coverings for him and for her.
Then God came down looking for where they might be,
but they were embarrassed and hid by a tree.

Now God said, "Why hide thee? Who told you to dress?"
To which Adam said, "Eve's the cause for this mess."
But Eve quickly answered to fend off the shame.
"The snake made me do it, so he is to blame."

Well, God cursed the snake on his belly to crawl,
and got really sad at the sense of man's fall.
But justice demanded He send them away,
and since then came suffering and sin, here to stay.

The beautiful Garden of Eden God closed,
since man and his wife due to sin were deposed.
He posted strong angels at all the ways in,
and no one has ever since entered again.

Cain and Abel

Genesis 4:1-16

Now Adam and Eve from the garden did go.
God told them to multiply, so they did so.
The first son was Cain who the parents did cradle.
They then had another son-he was named Abel.

Now Cain worked the fields growing crops from his seed;
He'd pick of the fruit and the grain he would knead.
In this way he helped the first family survive.
In those days it wasn't so easy to thrive.

His young brother Abel raised sheep and some goats.
He'd guard them and watch them and feed them their oats.
And as for the family, when they wanted meat,
He'd pick from the flock and they'd sit down to eat.

Now one day the brothers a gift to God brought.
In their ways they wanted to please Him, they thought.
Cain brought of the best fruits he found in the field,
and Abel the best lamb that his flock could yield.

Now God thought that Cain's gift was kind of OK,
but much preferred Abel's gift far and away.
At finding this out Cain became very mad.
God said, "Cain it's yours to do good or do bad."

Well, Cain chose the bad, not the good of his will,
and went after Abel, his brother to kill.
When God asked of Cain where his brother might be,
Cain asked, "Is it my job to watch after he?"

Now God knew the wrong Cain had done on that day,
and so in His wrath He sent Cain far away.
Away to a land with a name rather odd;
the place that He sent him to had the name Nod.

And you might think, too, that the name's a bit strange,
but God is real good at these things to arrange.
The meaning of Nod, if right now you are pondering,
fit with Cain's punishment, since it means "wandering."

7

Noah

Genesis 6:9-22

There were many more people now since the beginning,
but God was real sad 'cause the people were sinning.
Wherever He looked people did not obey,
so God made His mind up to sweep them away.

As God made His plan all of life to destroy,
man, woman and beast; every girl and each boy.
He noticed one man that in goodness had walked,
so God went down to him and with him He talked.

This man was named Noah and all through his days,
he obeyed God's laws and he followed God's ways.
So God said, "Hey, Noah since you did behave,
your wife, sons and their wives I'm going to save."

The next thing God told him was quite a surprise.
In fact, I think Noah wide opened his eyes.
God said, "Build an ark," which is quite a big boat.
"You're going to need it—you're going to float!"

He then told old Noah the ark how to make.
This ark would float high up, not just on a lake.
It must have three decks and a window and door,
for animals many will stand on the floor.

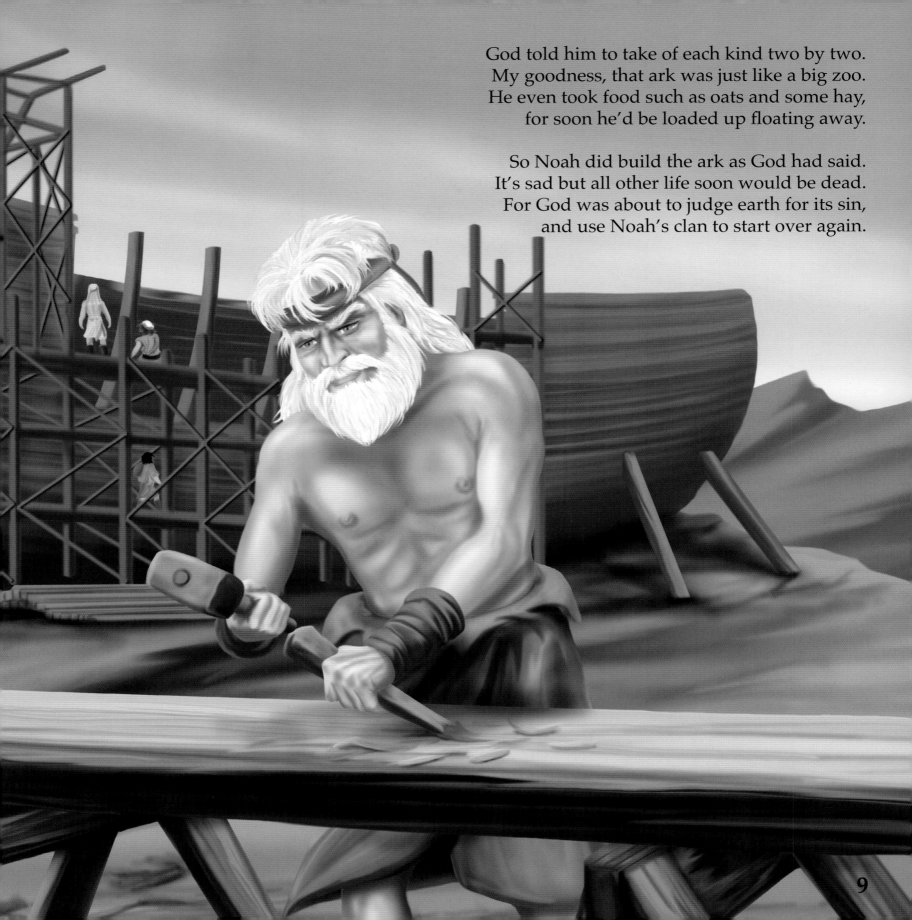

God told him to take of each kind two by two.
My goodness, that ark was just like a big zoo.
He even took food such as oats and some hay,
for soon he'd be loaded up floating away.

So Noah did build the ark as God had said.
It's sad but all other life soon would be dead.
For God was about to judge earth for its sin,
and use Noah's clan to start over again.

9

The Flood

Genesis 7:1-8:19; 9:8-17

Now all the time Noah was building the ark,
the town's people mocked him; they thought it a lark.
But Noah kept building just as God had said.
He knew that those doubters would soon all be dead.

He finished—then loaded up each kind by two.
A male and female all passed quickly through.
Though of the clean animals he took in seven,
just as God said when He spoke down from heaven.

Once all aboard with the lions and bears,
rodents and spiders and even some hares,
God reached down and on His own closed the door,
opened the skies and rain started to pour.

God had told Noah that He'd use a flood,
rise up the waters to end flesh and blood.
Forty days and nights the rain clouds did hover.
All of earth's mountains the water did cover.

Any with breath of life living on earth,
drowned in that great flood that God did give birth.
Waters subsided. Yes, God handled that,
'til the ark settled on Mount Ararat.

Noah for forty days then he did count,
sent out a raven, it flew 'round about.
Next, sent a dove let it out on his hand.
That dove came back 'cause it couldn't find land.

Seven more days and another dove flew,
never came back, land was dry now he knew.
Then God told Noah, his son's and their wives,
"All of you out, multiply, live your lives."

God made a promise then, not earth to flood.
Never again would rain end flesh and blood.
Said, "Here's a promise between earth and I,
sealed by a rainbow placed up in the sky."

Tower of Babel

Genesis 11:1-9

Now God had told Noah, his sons and their wives,
to spread out, have children and so live their lives.
They all then got moving, men, women and beast,
and settled in Shinar which was to the east.

Once there, all the men said, "Hey, let's build a city."
They wanted a tower, but oh what a pity,
the stones they were using were not very flat,
and you can't build tall things with round stones like that.

But lucky for them they learned how bricks to make.
These bricks were real square and were baked like a cake.
And yes, they could stack them way up in the sky.
They'd stick them with tar and they'd then let them dry.

"We're building a tower!" they'd proudly proclaim.
"We'll build it to heaven and so make our fame."
But God saw their doings and said, "This must stop.
Now what can I do to make this thing a flop?"

"I'll mess up their language—they won't understand,
then they'll go away and spread out through the land."
And that's what God did when He came down that day,
the tower did stop and the men moved away.

Now Babel they called the place where this occurred.
The languages changed and the meanings were blurred.
And that's why our languages differ today,
and how men at Shinar God moved on their way.

God Calls Abram

Genesis 12:1-10

Now many years passed after Noah's son Shem,
with children and grandkids again and again,
until finally born was a man name of Terah
who had a son Abram, and he married Sarai.

God called out to Abram while he lived in Haran,
said, "Pack up your bags now 'cause for you I'm carin'.
I'm going to make of you nations so grand,
but first you must move to a far away land."

So Abram obeyed, took his bags in his hand,
and then off he went to a land called Canaan.
And with him went Sarai and his nephew Lot,
with all the possessions in Haran they'd got.

In Moreh of Shechem they came to a tree,
and at that place Abram the Lord he did see.
God said, "To your children I will give this land,"
and Abram did worship at hearing God's plan.

Now there came a time when no food was aroun',
so then off to Egypt they then did go down.
And God did bless Abram there with many things,
as off he did go on his new wanderings.

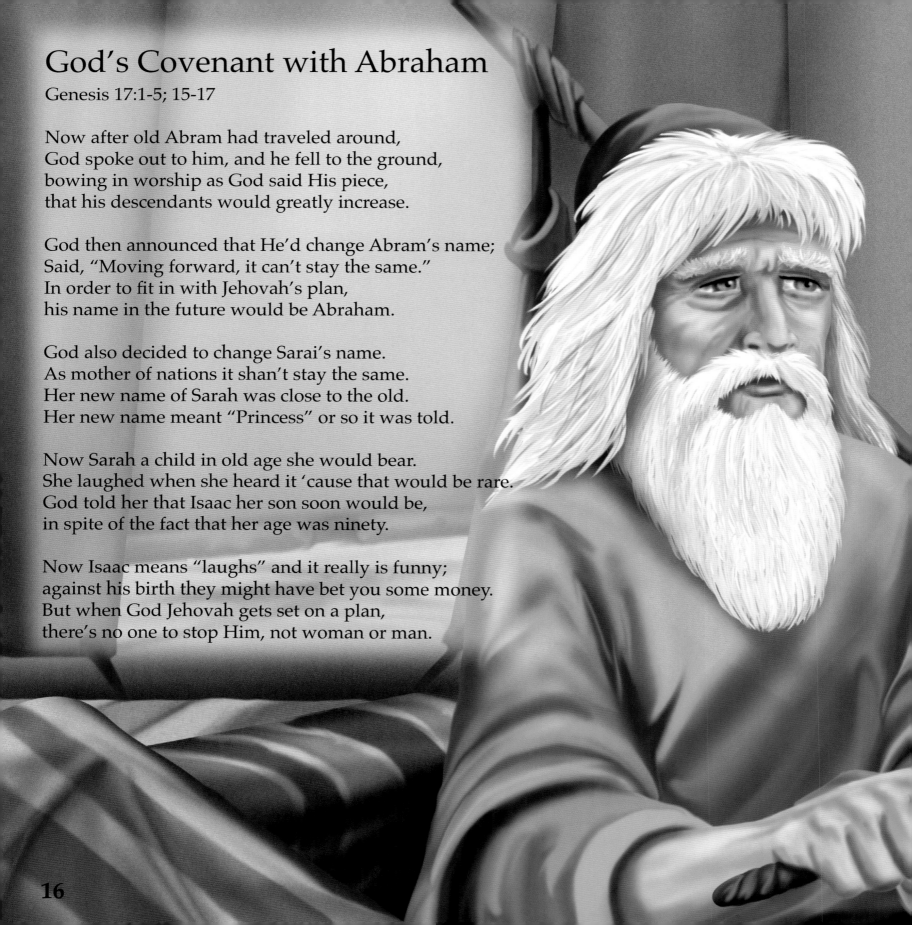

God's Covenant with Abraham

Genesis 17:1-5; 15-17

Now after old Abram had traveled around,
God spoke out to him, and he fell to the ground,
bowing in worship as God said His piece,
that his descendants would greatly increase.

God then announced that He'd change Abram's name;
Said, "Moving forward, it can't stay the same."
In order to fit in with Jehovah's plan,
his name in the future would be Abraham.

God also decided to change Sarai's name.
As mother of nations it shan't stay the same.
Her new name of Sarah was close to the old.
Her new name meant "Princess" or so it was told.

Now Sarah a child in old age she would bear.
She laughed when she heard it 'cause that would be rare.
God told her that Isaac her son soon would be,
in spite of the fact that her age was ninety.

Now Isaac means "laughs" and it really is funny;
against his birth they might have bet you some money.
But when God Jehovah gets set on a plan,
there's no one to stop Him, not woman or man.

Abraham Pleads for Sodom

Genesis 18:1-3; 16-33

One day the Lord and two angels came down,
speaking with Abraham—hanging around,
talking to him of the promises made
of his son Isaac, 'cause he had obeyed.

Then God decided to tell of a plan,
one that He'd normally hide from a man.
Seems sin in Sodom so bad was that day,
God had decided to sweep it away.

At this old Abraham did appear sad.
Asked, "Will you sweep away good with the bad?
What if there's fifty or forty-five good?"
"Then I will pass," said the Lord as He stood.

Abraham then said, "I pray, don't get mad.
Forty or thirty may not be that bad?"
God said, "If thirty good we find it so,
Sodom won't suffer, we'll turn and we'll go."

Abraham pleaded, said, "Lord if there be,
twenty or ten people standing rightly?"
"Even if ten," said the Lord God of all,
"if there are ten good the city won't fall."

Then that was it the discussion was through,
God went away as did Abraham too.
As for the Angels they went down the mount-
down to old Sodom the righteous to count.

Sodom and Gomorrah

Genesis 19:1-29

The Angels arrived there it was pretty late,
they found nephew Lot sitting down in the gate.
"Turn into my home wash your feet have no care."
The Angels said they'd rather sleep in the square.

The night proved that God was so right 'bout this city.
The people were sinners; it was such a pity.
There weren't even ten who were upright and good.
There soon would be ashes where this city stood.

Now up in the morning the Angels said, "Lot!"
Said, "Grab up your family and run from this spot.
Away to the mountains and don't dilly-dally,
for soon will be brimstone all over this valley."

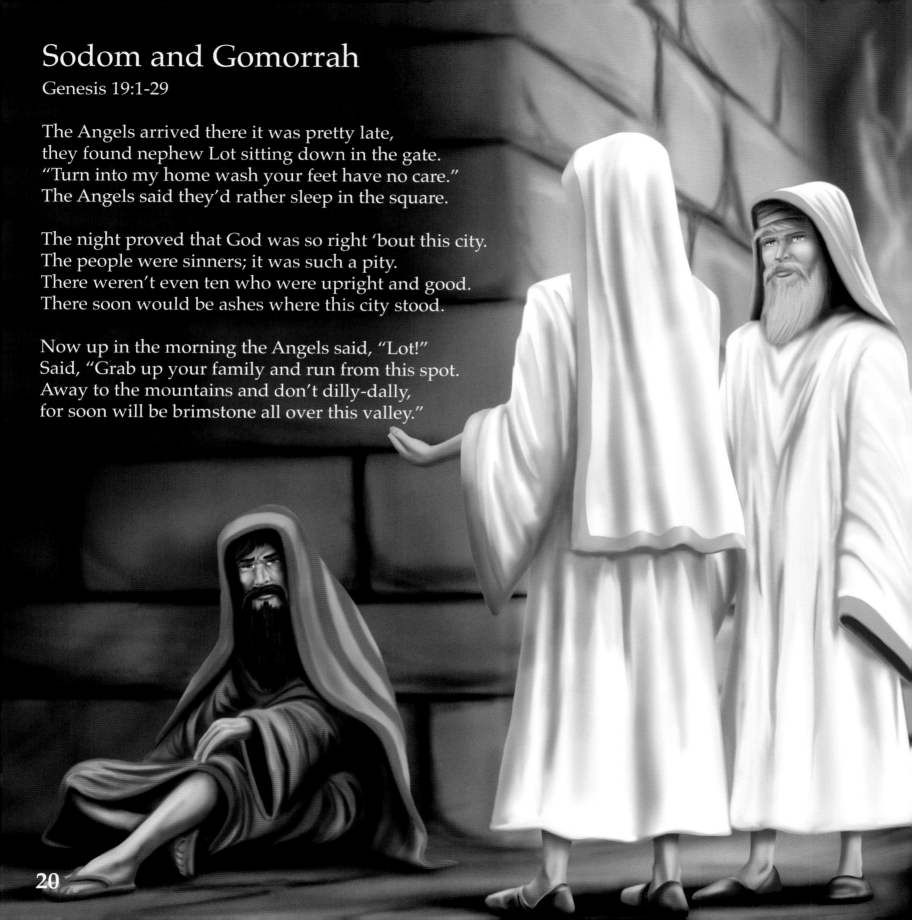

20

So Lot grabbed his wife and his two daughters too
and pulled them away just before ashes blew
For God rained down fire and brimstone in mass
and Lot's family ran up the hills, but ala...

Lot's wife ignored what the Angels had said
and she turned to salt because she turned her head
They'd said, "Don't look back, just run right up the hill
but she did not listen so God froze her stil...

Then Abraham looked down on all of the smok
God had to destroy them it was not a jok
But Abraham God did he honor that da
when Angels took Lot and his family awa...

Isaac-The Sacrifice

Genesis 22:1-18

Well some time had passed now since Isaac was born.
It seemed that from Abraham he would be torn.
'Cause God said, "Take Isaac, for whom you do care,
On up to a mount and you'll offer him there."

Now Abraham did just as God told him to.
He saddled a donkey and took some men too.
With Isaac his son and some wood there to burn,
He thought, back to God his son Isaac he'd turn.

In three days they got to the place God had showed.
The dad took the fire and the son took the load.
And up then they hiked to an offering make;
It still seemed that Isaac's life God would soon take.

In fact Isaac asked of the lamb, "Where is he?
For otherwise how can a sacrifice be?"
Then Abraham said, still not knowing God's plan,
"Be still now my son God will give us a lamb."

The alter they built, stacked the wood all around,
Then Abraham, Isaac with ropes he did bound.
He laid Isaac up on the top with great strife,
And then in his hand he did take up the knife.

But just as he raised it to finish God's plan,
An Angel of God said, "Now stop, Abraham.
You've showed that you fear Me by giving your son,
And as for the sacrifice, I'll give you one."

2

Then Abraham looked up and saw in a thorn,
a ram that had somehow got stuck by his horn.
So Abraham took it and made offering,
and God told again of the blessing He'd bring.

That Abraham's offspring would soon multiply;
their numbers would be as the stars in the sky.
And further God said, "As for all of the rest,"
"through you all the nations on earth will be blessed."

Jacob and Esau

Genesis 25:19-34

As Abraham moved toward the end of his life
He thought it the best to find Isaac a wife.
She came from a town name of Paddan Aram.
The name's kind of funny but that was God's plan.

Her name was Rebekah and pretty was she,
and babies inside she had one less than three.
In fact, they did wrestle so much she would tire,
she finally went to the Lord to inquire.

God said, "You do carry two peoples inside.
The boys with each other will never abide.
Two nations they'll form and though both will be bold,
the older will serve the young one," she was told.

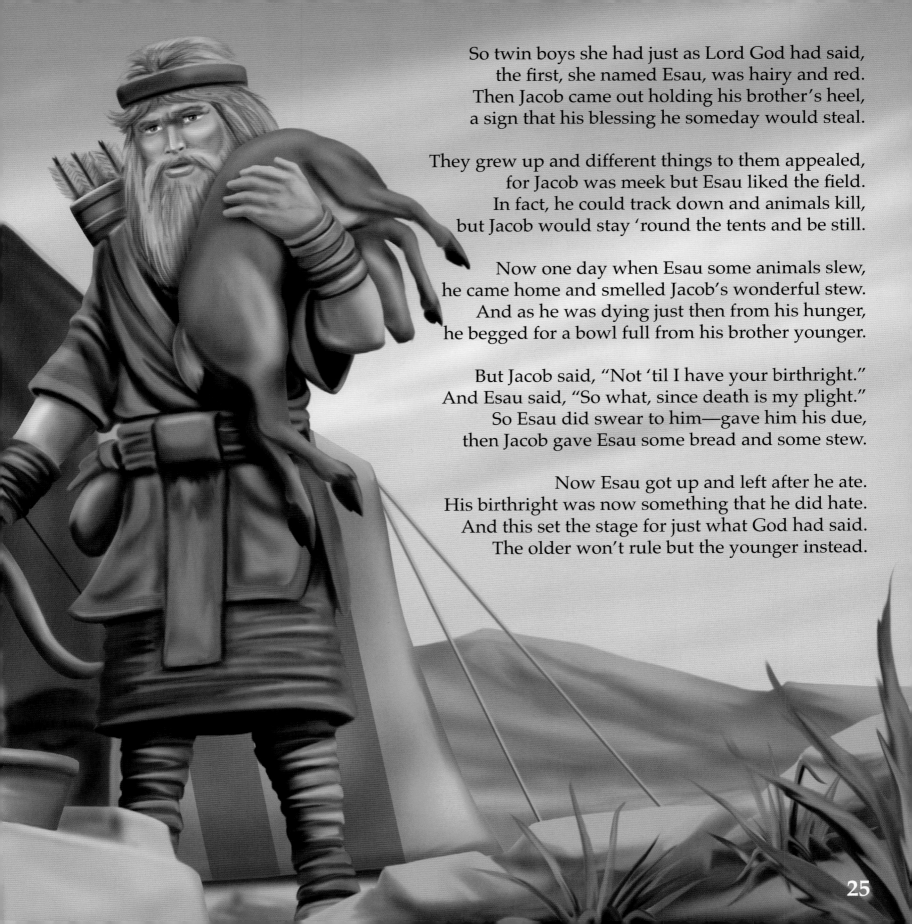

So twin boys she had just as Lord God had said,
the first, she named Esau, was hairy and red.
Then Jacob came out holding his brother's heel,
a sign that his blessing he someday would steal.

They grew up and different things to them appealed,
for Jacob was meek but Esau liked the field.
In fact, he could track down and animals kill,
but Jacob would stay 'round the tents and be still.

Now one day when Esau some animals slew,
he came home and smelled Jacob's wonderful stew.
And as he was dying just then from his hunger,
he begged for a bowl full from his brother younger.

But Jacob said, "Not 'til I have your birthright."
And Esau said, "So what, since death is my plight."
So Esau did swear to him—gave him his due,
then Jacob gave Esau some bread and some stew.

Now Esau got up and left after he ate.
His birthright was now something that he did hate.
And this set the stage for just what God had said.
The older won't rule but the younger instead.

Joseph

Genesis 37:1-35

Well, Jacob got married and many kids had.
Of the nation Israel he'd be called dad,
since each of the twelve tribes do in his clan run,
and one of his kids was named Joseph—his son.

Now Joseph was famous for stealing the stage.
He'd been born to Jacob in Jacob's old age.
Though loved by his father and maybe some others,
young Joseph was hated by all of his brothers.

In fact over Joseph his father would gloat,
he even gave Joseph a colorful coat.
That coat will be used as you'll see later on,
in lies told to Jacob 'bout why Joseph's gone.

So, as stories go, Joseph dreamed of some things,
not lions or tigers or birdies with wings,
but sheaves of grain, 'leven stars, sun and a moon,
and how they would all bow to him pretty soon.

Now at this the brothers a tantrum did pitch,
and when chance provided threw him in a ditch.
They then to some travelers young Joseph sold,
put blood on his coat and a story they told.

They said of the blood on his coat they had spilled,
"It must be by animals Joseph was killed."
And Jacob believed every word that they said.
and grieved at his loss as he lay in his bed.

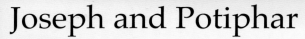

Joseph and Potiphar

Genesis 39:1-23

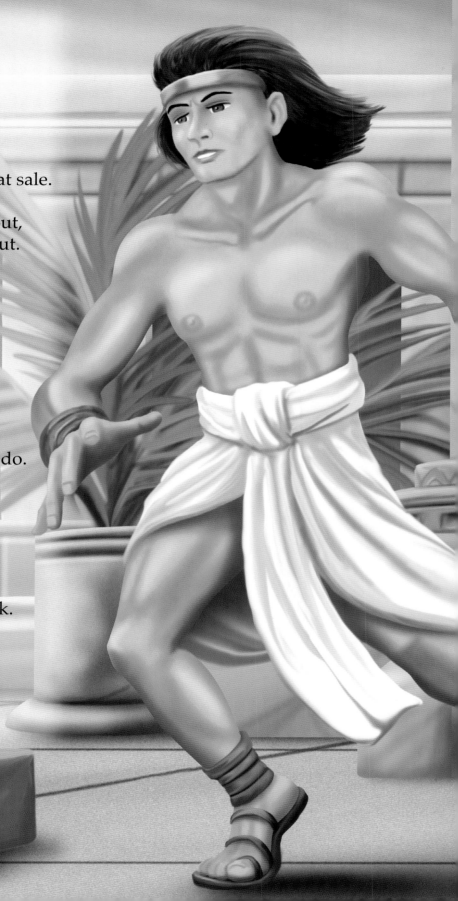

Now Joseph was taken to Egypt, it's told,
and to a strong man in the kingdom was sold.
The man name of Potiphar—head of the jail,
was pleased when he saw what he'd bought in that sale.

He noticed straight way that God helped Joseph out,
and blessed him in all ways there were round about.
So Potiphar gave him charge o'r all his things,
and God in return gave to him all blessings.

Now Joseph was young and a good looking lad,
and as a result faced a thing very bad,
when Potiphar's wife came to Joseph and said,
"I want you to come up to me in my bed."

But Joseph refused as he spoke to her true,
"This thing that you're asking would be wrong to do.
Your husband has given me charge o'r his stuff."
Then Potiphar's wife would just get in a huff.

Now one day alone in the house were the two,
and Potiphar's wife had him this time, she knew.
Well Joseph did run as he thought this no joke,
but she grabbed his garment—they called it a cloak.

Then Potiphar's wife told the biggest of lies;
not how for young Joseph that she did have eyes.
Instead she said Joseph had come after her,
and as you might think this caused quite a big stir.

Young Joseph was taken, the Bible does tell,
right down to the dungeon and put in a cell.
But God blessed him there again—He did not fail,
and Joseph soon 'nough was in charge of the jail.

This story does teach us that though sin seems fun,
when something is wrong, turn away and just run.
For God watches over those who pass these tests,
and surely through life those like Joseph are blessed.

29

The Cupbearer and Baker

Genesis 40:1-23; 41:1-32

Now some time had passed there with Joseph in jail,
but his God was with him, He never did fail,
right up until two men the King did offend,
and off to the jail both of them did he send.

It's said that the baker and one who cups bear,
in work for the King before they were sent there,
did somehow offend the dear King in their jobs,
which led them to prison and likely brought sobs.

Well Joseph was then put in charge of these two,
and they both had dreams—what they meant, no one knew.
But you may remember from stories now past,
that Joseph a dreamer was too at long last.

Well Joseph did tell what the dreams for them meant.
The answers he got, straight from God they were sent.
The bearer of cups in three days would be free.
The baker instead would be hanged on a tree.

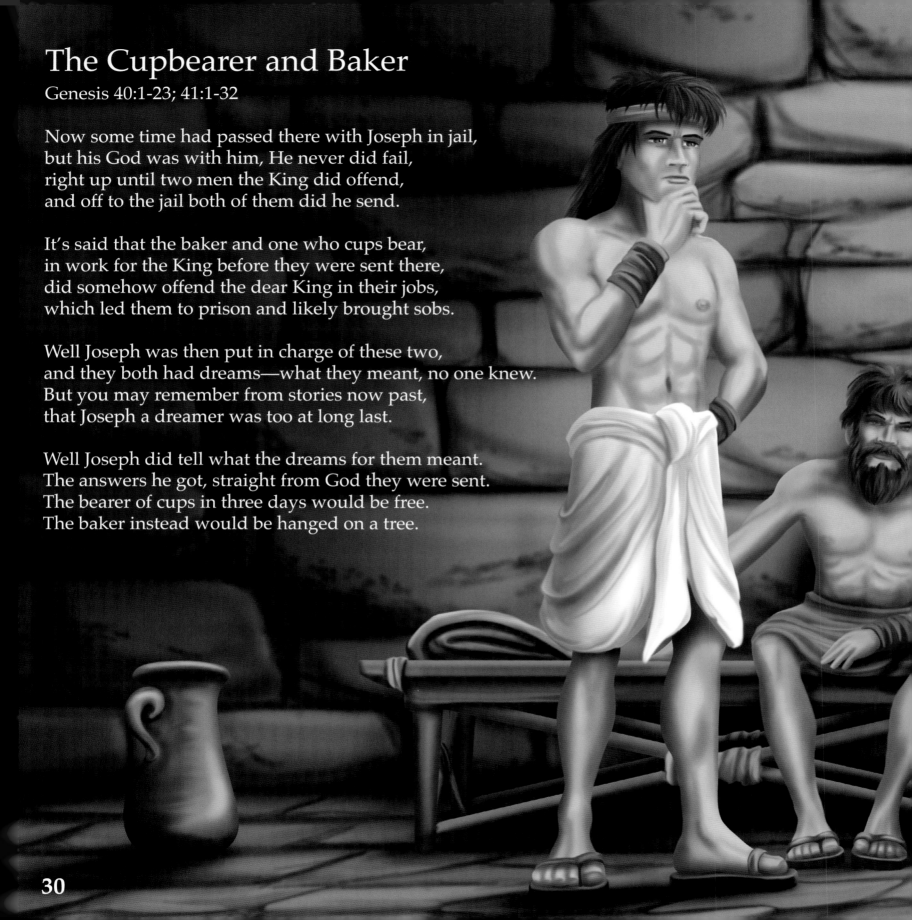

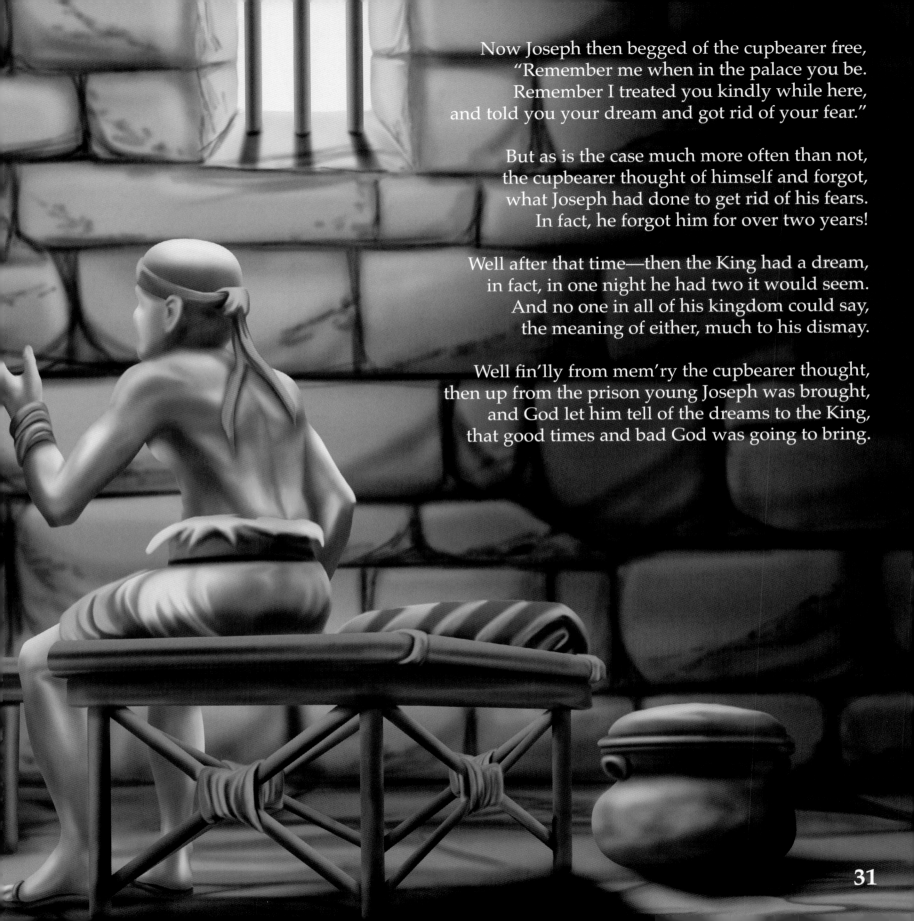

Now Joseph then begged of the cupbearer free,
"Remember me when in the palace you be.
Remember I treated you kindly while here,
and told you your dream and got rid of your fear."

But as is the case much more often than not,
the cupbearer thought of himself and forgot,
what Joseph had done to get rid of his fears.
In fact, he forgot him for over two years!

Well after that time—then the King had a dream,
in fact, in one night he had two it would seem.
And no one in all of his kingdom could say,
the meaning of either, much to his dismay.

Well fin'lly from mem'ry the cupbearer thought,
then up from the prison young Joseph was brought,
and God let him tell of the dreams to the King,
that good times and bad God was going to bring.

Joseph Gets the Job

Genesis 41:25-45:8

So Joseph with two more years in jail spent,
told Pharaoh of Egypt just what his dreams meant.
Then Joseph reminded him, "I'm just a man,
the dreams are from God telling you of a plan."

The plan was for seven years food would grow great;
there'd be much abundance, this was Egypt's fate.
But seven years following would not be good,
in fact there'd be dirt right where wheat once had stood.

They call this a famine when food can't be found.
It happens when no drops of rain hit the ground.
So Joseph said, "Find a good man—not corrupt,
who during the good years much food will store up."

Well Pharaoh said, "How can there be such a man,
as this young man Joseph who told me God's plan?"
So second to Pharaoh young Joseph became,
and in years to come, this brought him much fame.

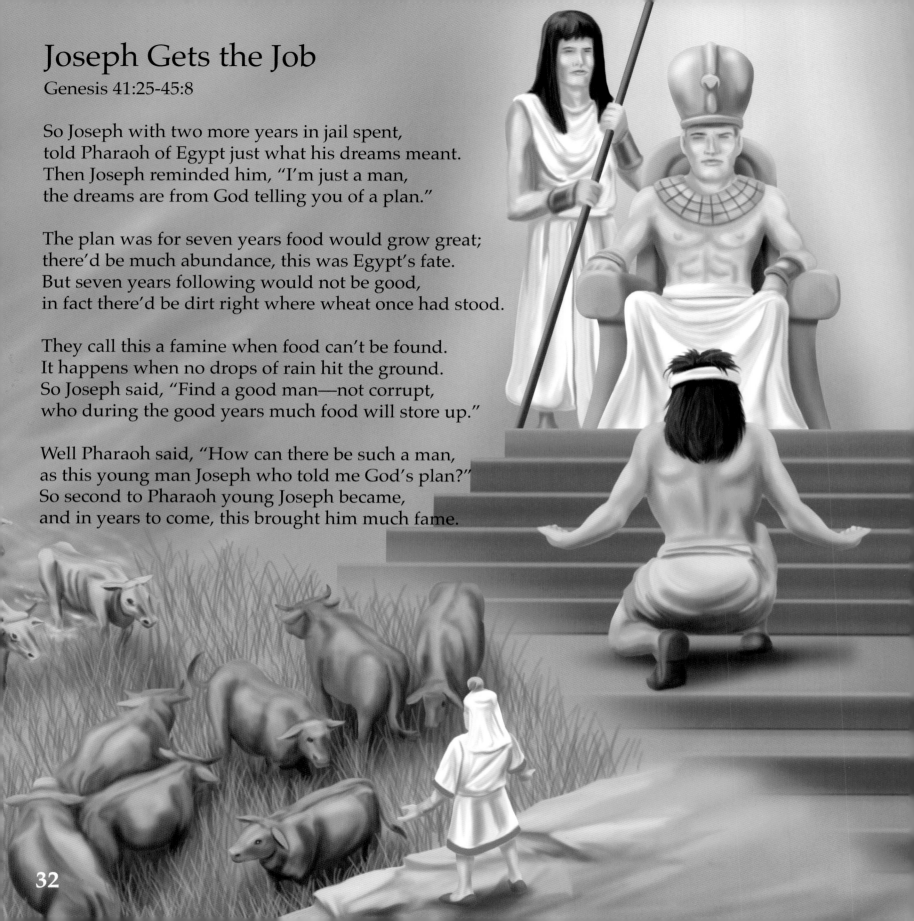

Now after the famine had gotten quite bad,
it seems Joseph's brothers were really quite sad.
You see, they too lacked any food left to eat,
so Jacob their father said, "Get to your feet!"

Said, "Go down to Egypt and buy us some wheat."
And who there do you think that they had to meet?
That's right, it was Joseph the brother they'd sold,
but they didn't know him and they were not told,

'Till after two trips when the brothers were back,
because Joseph placed money back in their sack.
They were fin'lly told that this man was their brother,
at which time they all looked with fear at each other.

You see, they thought Joseph would mad at them be,
for selling him off to some foreign country.
But Joseph said, "No—'cause what you meant for bad,
my God meant for good so instead I'm quite glad!"

33

Jacob to Egypt

Genesis 45:16-47:1

Now after these things Joseph sent for his dad,
to move him to Egypt with all that he had,
with all of his children and all of his flocks,
but he didn't need to bring clothes or his socks.

See, Pharaoh was happy to hear of this thing,
and told Joseph they need not those things to bring.
He told him that all brand new stuff they would get,
so for Jacob's fam'ly was everything set.

Well Jacob was happy as happy can be,
for Joseph his son he was anxious to see.
You see—don't forget he thought Joseph was dead,
and now he finds out he's a ruler instead.

He stopped at Beersheba while on the way down,
and sacrifice made as he fell to the groun'.
That night in a vision he heard his God call.
He said, "I am God of your fathers and all."

God told him to go down without any fear.
He said he would bless him then bring him back here.
Told Jacob the same He'd told Isaac was sure,
And grandfather Abraham way back in Ur.

That from them a very great nation He'd make.
He'd fulfill the promise just for His name's sake.
So Jacob went down and with Joseph he met.
They cried out of happiness 'til they were wet.

And that's where they lived then for many more years.
God blessed them and they lived without any fears.
In Goshen they settled—a stop on the way,
to Canaan where they would go back to someday.

Jacob's Death

Genesis 48:1-50:26

Now Jacob grew older and was soon to die.
He called his son Joseph said, "Touch here my thigh.
I want you to swear that when I breathe no more,
you'll bury me back where I once lived before."

So Joseph did swear so to Israel that day-
Oh my, I just realized we forgot to say;
God changed Jacob's name due to their strong relation,
He now called him Israel, the name of his nation.

Well prior to dying he blessed Joseph's sons.
It's truly amazing how God does have fun.
You see, just as Jacob the younger was blessed,
he blessed Joseph's younger before all the rest.

Next Israel blessed all of the others then too.
The blessings all fit just as God willed them to.
So Reuben then Simeon and Levi were first.
The latter two due to their hatred were cursed.

Then Judah was praised and to his line it came,
that someday Messiah would come down and reign.
Next Zebulun, Issachar, Dan and then Gad,
with some blessings good but then some were quite bad.

Then Asher and Naphtali both received good,
and finally Joseph and Benjamin stood.
And then, that was it, all twelve blessings were done,
and Jacob said, "My grave's the field of Ephron."

And that's just what happened once he breathed his last.
They took him to right where his fathers had passed.
So Abraham, Isaac and Jacob were gone,
but God still remembered all that had gone on.

He prospered their children in Egypt you see,
they multiplied greatly like sand of the sea,
until all the brothers and Joseph were dead,
and by a new King all of Egypt was led.